THIS BOOK BELONGS TO:

from SEA *to* SHINING SEA

p

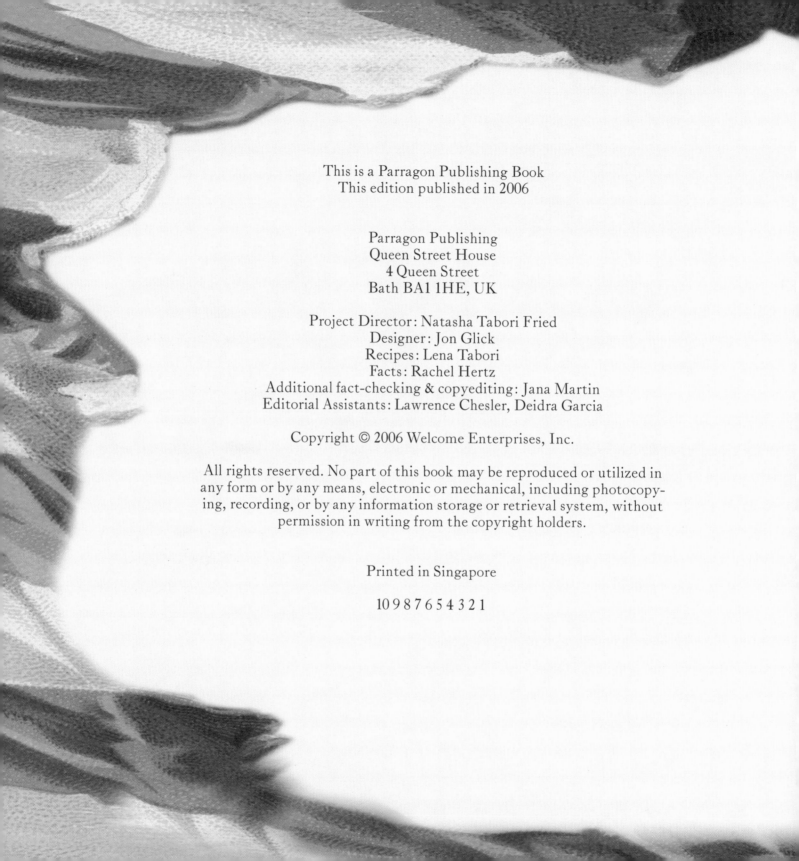

This is a Parragon Publishing Book
This edition published in 2006

Parragon Publishing
Queen Street House
4 Queen Street
Bath BA1 1HE, UK

Project Director: Natasha Tabori Fried
Designer: Jon Glick
Recipes: Lena Tabori
Facts: Rachel Hertz
Additional fact-checking & copyediting: Jana Martin
Editorial Assistants: Lawrence Chesler, Deidra Garcia

Printed in Singapore

10 9 8 7 6 5 4 3 2 1

CONTENTS

THE WHOLE WORLD IS COMING

LAKOTA GHOST DANCE SONG, CIRCA 1880

The whole world is coming.
A nation is coming, a nation is coming,
The Eagle has brought the message to the tribe.
The father says so, the father says so.
Over the whole earth they are coming.
The buffalo are coming, the buffalo are coming,
The crow has brought the message to the tribe,
The father says so, the father says so.

POWHATAN TO CAPTAIN JOHN SMITH

JAMESTOWN, VIRGINIA, 1609

Despite the life-saving aid that Powhatan Confederacy tribes gave the first English settlers in Jamestown, the settlers abused the friendship. Conflicts arose over land and the trading of weapons and food. Powhatan (Chief Wahunsonacock), chief of the Powhatan Confederacy and the father of Pocahontas, addressed Captain John Smith with this warning.

I AM NOW GROWN OLD, and must soon die; and the succession must descend, in order, to my brothers, Opitchapan, Opekankanough, and Catataugh, and then to my two sisters, and their two daughters. I wish their experience was equal to mine; and that your love to us might not be less than ours to you.

Why should you take by force that from us which you can have by love? Why should you destroy us, who have provided you with food? What can you get by war? We can hide our provisions, and fly into the woods; and then you must consequently famish by wronging your friends. What is the cause of your jealousy? You see us unarmed, and willing to supply your wants, if you will come in a friendly manner, and not with swords and guns, as to invade an enemy.

I am not so simple, as not to know it is better to eat good meat, lie well, and sleep quietly with my women and children; to laugh and be merry with the English; and, being their friend, to have copper, hatchets, and whatever else I want, than to fly from all, to lie cold in the woods, feed upon acorns, roots, and such trash, and to be so hunted, that I cannot rest, eat, or sleep. In such circumstances, my men must watch, and if a twig should but break, all would cry out, "Here comes Captain Smith"; and so, in this miserable manner, to end my miserable life; and, Captain Smith, this might be soon your fate too, through your rashness and unadvisedness.

I, therefore, exhort you to peaceable councils; and, above all, I insist that the guns and swords, the cause of all our jealousy and uneasiness, be removed and sent away.

The Wild West

On October 26, 1881, the Earp brothers (Wyatt, Virgil, and Morgan) and Doc Holliday faced down the Clanton Gang in a 30-second hail of bullets behind the OK Corral in Tombstone, Arizona. When it was over, Virgil and Morgan were wounded and three outlaws lay dead.

Doc Holliday (1851–1887) was a dentist by trade who moved West for his health.

Wyatt Earp (1848–1929) was a gambler and a law man who roamed the West from Illinois to Alaska.

Born Martha Jane Cannary in Princeton, Missouri, Calamity Jane (1852–1903) was orphaned as a young girl. She made her way working anywhere from mining camps to dance halls. A drinker, talker and smoker who shot like a man, she claimed to have married Wild Bill Hickok.

There was truth to the legends surrounding Wild Bill Hickok (1837–1876): a farmhand, stagecoach driver and hired gun, he worked as a Union army spy and served as a Marshall on the rough frontier after the Civil War.

Crazy Horse (1844–1877), chief of the Oglala Sioux, refused to be pushed onto a reservation. He united Sioux and Cheyenne forces to defeat General Custer and his troops at Little Bighorn, but ultimately surrendered in order to survive.

Geronimo (1829–1909), though not a chief, was recognized as a leader of the Chiricahua Apache. After being forced onto a barren reservation in Arizona, he led a number of revolts. Years of conflict ended in Geronimo's surrender, and he died in detention.

General George Armstrong Custer (1839–1876) earned his reputation in the campaigns against the Indians in South Dakota and Montana, as well as in the Civil War. He was killed at Little Bighorn, where his men were defeated by Lakota, Cheyenne and Arapaho warriors.

Teton Sioux Chief Sitting Bull (1831–1890) was instrumental in annihilating General Custer's attacking forces, but lived on to see his people surrender and move to reservations. Late in his life, he traveled with Buffalo Bill's Wild West show.

"Buffalo" Bill Cody (1846–1917) was a champion buffalo hunter, army scout and founder of Buffalo Bill's Wild West, a traveling show that began the rodeo and toured America and Europe.

O PIONEERS!
WILLA CATHER, 1913

ALEXANDRA DREW HER SHAWL CLOSER about her and stood leaning against the frame of the mill, looking at the stars which glittered so keenly through the frosty autumn air. She always loved to watch them, to think of their vastness and distance, and of their ordered march. It fortified her to reflect upon the great operations of nature, and when she thought of the law that lay behind them, she felt a sense of personal security. That night she had a new consciousness of the country, felt almost a new relation to it. Even her talk with the boys had not taken away the feeling that had overwhelmed her when she drove back to the Divide that afternoon. She had never known before how much the country meant to her. The chirping of the insects down in the long grass had been like the sweetest music. She had felt as if her heart were hiding down there, somewhere, with the quail and the plover and all the little wild things that crooned or buzzed in the sun. Under the long shaggy ridges, she felt the future stirring.

BARBECUED RIBS

American barbecue was first popularized on the cattle drives of the late 1800s, when cowboys slow-roasted tough meat to make it more palatable. The barbecue sauce was created using a New World staple: tomatoes.

3 cups ketchup

1 cup chili sauce

grated zest of 1 lemon

Juice of 2 large lemon

$1/4$ cup French's mustard

1 $1/2$ tablespoons Tabasco sauce

$1/4$ cup Worcestershire sauce

2 tablespoons molasses

2 tablespoons brown sugar

2 cloves garlic, chopped

$1/4$ cup chopped parsley

2 tablespoons apple cider vinegar

salt and pepper to taste

3 pounds beef ribs

1. In a large heavy skillet, combine all of the ingredients (except the ribs) and warm through over low heat. Do not bring to a boil.

2. Remove, cool and use half the mixture to rub all sides of the meat 1 hour before grilling.

3. Prepare the grill and ignite the charcoal.

4. Grill the ribs over medium–hot coals until tender (1 hour or so). Keep basting and make sure you turn them frequently so they don't burn.

5. Continue cooking for 20–25 minutes until done. (You can also do these in the oven: preheat oven to 325° F and place the ribs in a shallow baking pan. Cover with half the sauce. Bake in the center of the oven for 1–1 $1/2$ hour depending on the size. Turn and baste frequently with the remaining sauce.)

Serves 6 to 8.

Potato Salad

$^1/_3$ cup chicken stock

2 tablespoons cider vinegar

2 pounds large potatoes, peeled, cooked and sliced

1 cup mayonnaise

2 tablespoons Dijon mustard

$^2/_3$ cup finely chopped scallions

$^1/_2$ cup finely chopped celery

3 tablespoons or so finely chopped fresh chives

salt and pepper to taste

1. Mix the chicken stock and the vinegar and pour over the potatoes.

2. In a separate bowl, mix the mayonnaise and Dijon mustard. Add the scallions, celery and chives. Combine with the potatoes, mixing gently.

3. Season to taste with salt and pepper.

4. Cover and refrigerate for at least an hour. Let stand at room temperature for 20 minutes before serving.

5. Serve with barbecued ribs and slices of fresh watermelon.

Serves 4 to 6.

BATTLE HYMN OF THE REPUBLIC

JULIA WARD HOWE, 1862

Mine eyes have seen the glory of the coming of the Lord:
He is trampling out the vintage where the grapes of wrath are stored;
He hath loosed the fateful lightning of his terrible swift sword:
   His truth is marching on.

   Chorus
   Glory, glory hallelujah,
   Glory, glory hallelujah,
   Glory, glory hallelujah,
   His truth is marching on.

I have seen Him in the watch-fires of a hundred circling camps;
They have builded Him an altar in the evening dews and damps;
I can read His righteous sentence by the dim and flaring lamps.
   His day is marching on.

I have read a fiery gospel, writ in burnished rows of steel:
"As ye deal with my contemners, so with you my grace shall deal;
Let the Hero, born of woman, crush the serpent with his heel,
   Since God is marching on."

He has sounded forth the trumpet that shall never call retreat;
He is sifting out the hearts of men before His judgment-seat:
Oh! be swift, my soul, to answer Him! be jubilant, my feet!
    Our God is marching on.

In the beauty of the lilies Christ was born across the sea,
With a glory in his bosom that transfigures you and me:
As he died to make men holy, let us die to make men free,
    While God is marching on.

WILLIAM COBBETT
TO MISS RACHEL SMITHERS

PHILADELPHIA, JULY 6, 1794

Like many English, William Cobbett arrived in America in 1792 with high hopes. In an excerpt from his letter to friend Rachel Smithers back in England, he expressed his disappointment.

This country is good for getting money, that is to say, if a person is industrious and enterprising. In every other respect the country is miserable. Exactly the contrary of what I expected. The land is bad, rocky; houses wretched; roads impassable after the least rain. Fruit in quantity, but good for nothing. One apple or peach in England or France is worth a bushel of them here. The seasons are detestable. All is burning or freezing. There is no spring or autumn. The weather is so very inconstant that you are never sure for an hour, a single hour at a time. Last night we made a fire to sit by, and to-day it is scorching hot. The whole month of March was so hot that we could hardly bear our clothes, and three parts of the month of June there was frost every night, and so cold in the

day-time that we were obliged to wear great-coats. The people are worthy of the country—cheating, sly, roguish gang. Strangers make fortunes here in spite of all this, particularly the English. The natives are by nature idle, and seek to live by cheating, while foreigners, being industrious, seek no other means than those dictated by integrity, and are sure to meet with encouragement even from the idle and roguish themselves; for, however roguish a man may be, he always loves to deal with an honest man. You have perhaps heard of the plague being at Philadelphia last year. It was no plague; it was a fever of the country, and is by no means extra-ordinary among the Americans. In the fall of the year almost every person, in every place, has a spell of fever that is called fall-fever. It is often fatal, and the only way to avoid it is to quit the country. But this fever is not all. Every month has its particular malady. In July, for example, everybody almost, or at least one half of the people, are taken with vomitings for several days at a time; they often carry off the patient, and almost always children. In short, the country is altogether detestable....

Wm. Cobbett

The American Revolution

The Boston Tea Party—a protest against British taxes and Britain's monopoly on the tea trade on December 16th of 1773—involved colonists boarding British ships dressed as Mohawk Indians and dumping 342 crates of tea into Boston Harbor. What sort of tea? Darjeeling.

A leader in the American Revolution, Samuel Adams (1722–1803) was a founder of the Sons of Liberty, organized the Boston Tea Party and signed the Declaration of Independence.

As an express rider for the Massachusetts Committee of Safety, silversmith Paul Revere (1734–1818) took two heroic rides. During the first—in December 1774— he warned New Hampshire of a potential British landing.

Immortalized in verse by Longfellow, Revere's more famous ride took place April 18, 1775, when he raced to Lexington to warn that the British were headed for Concord. He was caught, but fellow rider William Dawes made it through. When the British arrived, the Minutemen were there to meet them. The shots fired began the war.

Patriot, lawyer and Virginia governor Patrick Henry (1736–1799) uttered the words "Give me liberty or give me death," and was largely responsible for correcting the new Constitution's shortcomings with the Bill of Rights.

Thomas Jefferson's first draft of the Declaration of Independence included a passage blaming George III for the slave trade. Congress struck it out.

Founding father Alexander Hamilton (1757–1804), the country's first treasury secretary, was killed in a duel with political opponent Aaron Burr.

Seamstress Betsy Ross (1752–1836) was asked by George Washington to sew the first American flag in May, 1776. The original little resembles the current flag, but the stars and stripes were present from the beginning.

It's said that John Hancock (1737–1793) made his signature on the Declaration of Independence big enough for the British king to read without putting on his glasses.

After the war, Noah Webster (1758–1843) created the first genuinely American Dictionary: *A Compendious Dictionary of the English Language* (1806).

Though we celebrate on July 4th, the colonies actually voted for independence July 2, 1776, and the Declaration of Independence wasn't signed by all members of Congress until August 2.

The war ended October 19, 1781, in Yorktown, Virginia. There, Lord Cornwallis surrendered to George Washington and French General Comte de Rochambeau.

GIVE ME LIBERTY OR GIVE ME DEATH

PATRICK HENRY, RICHMOND, VIRGINIA, MARCH 23, 1775

*Patrick Henry, a self-taught lawyer, stood up before a meeting
of 122 delegates and virtually galvanized the room into revolution.*

MR. PRESIDENT, it is natural to man to indulge in the illusions of hope. We are apt to shut our eyes against a painful truth, and listen to the song of that siren till she transforms us into beasts. Is this the part of wise men, engaged in a great and arduous struggle for liberty? Are we disposed to be of the number of those who, having eyes, see not, and, having ears, hear not, the things which so nearly concern their temporal salvation? For my part, whatever anguish of spirit it may cost, I am willing to know the whole truth, to know the worst, and to provide for it....

Sir, we have done everything that could be done, to avert the storm which is now coming on. We have petitioned, we have remonstrated, we have supplicated, we have prostrated ourselves before the throne, and have implored its interposition to arrest the tyrannical hands of the ministry and parliament. Our petitions have been slighted, our remonstrances have produced additional violence and insult, our supplications have been disregarded, and we have been spurned with contempt from the foot of the throne! In vain, after these things, may we indulge the fond hope of peace and reconciliation. There is no longer any room for hope. If we wish to be free, if we mean to preserve inviolate those inestimable privileges for which we have been so long contending, if we mean not basely to abandon the noble struggle in which we have been so long engaged, and which we have pledged ourselves never to abandon until the glorious object of our contest shall be obtained, we must fight! I repeat it, sir, we must fight! An appeal to arms and to the God of Hosts is all that is left us.

They tell us, sir, that we are weak, unable to cope with so formidable an adversary. But when shall we be stronger? Will it be the next week or the next year? Will it be when we are totally disarmed, and when a British guard shall be stationed in every house? Shall we gather strength by irresolution and inaction? Shall we acquire the means of effectual resistance, by lying supinely on our backs, and hugging the delusive phantom of hope until our enemies shall have bound us hand and foot? Sir, we are not weak, if we make proper use of those means which the God of nature hath placed in our power. Three millions of people, armed in the holy cause of liberty, and in such a country as that which we possess, are invincible by any force which our enemy can send against us. Besides, sir, we shall not fight our battles alone. There is a just God who presides over the destinies of nations, and who will raise up friends to fight our battles for us. The battle, sir, is not to the strong alone; it is to the vigilant, the active, the brave. Besides, sir, we have no election. If we were base enough to desire it, it is now too late to retire from the contest. There is no retreat but in submission and slavery! Our chains are forged! Their clanking may be heard on the plains of Boston! The war is inevitable—and let it come! I repeat, sir, let it come!

It is in vain, sir, to extenuate the matter. Gentlemen may cry, Peace, Peace, but there is no peace. The next gale that sweeps from the north will bring to our ears the clash of resounding arms! Our brethren are already in the field! Why stand we here idle? What is it that gentlemen wish? What would they have? Is life so dear, or peace so sweet, as to be purchased at the price of chains and slavery? Forbid it, Almighty God! I know not what course others may take, but as for me, give me liberty or give me death!

George Washington to Martha Washington

Philadelphia, June 18, 1775

When the American Rebels decided to take on the crown for independence, they nominated George Washington to be "Commander of All Continental Forces," at the Second Continental Congress in the summer of 1775. He accepted the challenge to turn the ragged and inexperienced group of men into a fighting force, but refused any pay. Three days later, Washington wrote to his wife, Martha, about his appointment.

My Dearest:

I am now set down to write to you on a subject which fills me with inexpressible concern, and this concern is greatly aggravated and increased, when I reflect upon the uneasiness I know it will give you. It has been determined in Congress, that the whole army raised for the defense of the American cause shall be put under my care, and that it is necessary for me to proceed immediately to Boston to take upon me the command of it.

You may believe me, my dear Patsy, when I assure you, in the most solemn manner that, so far from seeking this appointment, I have used every endeavor in my power to avoid it, not only from my unwillingness to part with you and the family, but from consciousness of its being a trust too great for my capacity, and that I should enjoy more real happiness in one month with you at home, than I have the most distant prospect of finding abroad, if my stay were to be seven times seven years. But as it has been a kind of destiny, that has thrown me upon this service, I shall hope that my undertaking is designed to answer some good purpose. You might, and I suppose did perceive, from the tenor of my letters, that I was apprehensive I could not avoid this appointment, as I did not pretend to intimate when I should return. That was the case. It was utterly out of my power to refuse this appointment, without exposing my character to such censures, as would have reflected dishonor upon myself, and given pain to my friends. This, I am sure, could not, and ought not, to be pleasing to you, and must have lessened me considerably in my own esteem. I shall rely, therefore, confidently on that Providence, which has heretofore preserved and been bountiful to me, not doubting but that I shall return safe to you in the fall. I shall feel no pain from the toil or the danger of the campaign; my unhappiness will flow from the uneasiness I know you will feel from being left alone. I therefore beg, that you will summon your whole fortitude, and pass your time as agreeably as possible....

As life is always uncertain, and common prudence dictates to every man the necessity of settling his temporal concerns, while it is in his power, and while the mind is calm and undisturbed, I have, since I came to this place (for I had not the time to do it before I left home) got Colonel Pendleton to draft a will for me, by the directions I gave him, which will I now enclose. The provision made for you in case of my death will, I hope, be agreeable.

I shall add nothing more, as I have several letters to write, but to desire that you will remember me to your friends, and to assure you that I am with the most unfeigned regard, my dear Patsy, your affectionate, &c.

G. Washington

Presidents

George Washington (no party affiliation), served 1789–1797

John Adams (Federalist), served 1797–1801

Thomas Jefferson (Democratic-Republican), served 1801–1809

James Madison (D-R), served 1809–1817

James Monroe (D-R), served 1817–1825

John Quincy Adams (D-R), served 1825–1829

Andrew Jackson (D), served 1829–1837

Martin Van Buren (D), served 1837–1841

William Henry Harrison (Whig), served March 1841–April 4,1841 (died of pneumonia in office)

John Tyler (Whig), served 1841–1845.

James Knox Polk (D), served 1845–1849

Zachary Taylor (Whig), served March 1849–July 9, 1850 (died of illness in office)

Millard Fillmore (Whig), served 1850–1853

Franklin Pierce (D), served 1853–1857

James Buchanan (D), served 1857–1861

Abraham Lincoln (R), served March 1861–April 15, 1865 (assassinated in office)

Andrew Johnson (National Union), served 1865–1869

Ulysses S. Grant (R), served 1869–1877

Rutherford B. Hayes (R), served 1877–1881

James A. Garfield (R), served March 1881–September 17, 1881 (assassinated in office)

Chester A. Arthur (R), served 1881–1885

Grover Cleveland (D), served 1885–1889

Benjamin Harrison (R), served 1889–1893

Grover Cleveland (D), served 1893–1897

William Mckinley (R), served March 1897–September 14, 1901 (assassinated in office)

Theodore Roosevelt (R), served 1901–1909

William H. Taft (R), served 1909–1913

Woodrow Wilson (D), served 1913–1921

Warren G. Harding (R), served March 1921–August 2, 1923 (died of a heart attack in office)

Calvin Coolidge (R), served 1923–1929

Herbert C. Hoover (R), served 1929–1933

Franklin D. Roosevelt (D), served March 1933–April 12, 1945 (died of a cerebral hemorrhage in office)

Harry S. Truman (D), served 1945–1953

Dwight David Eisenhower (R), served 1953–1961

John F. Kennedy (D), served January 1961–November 22, 1963 (assassinated in office)

Lyndon B. Johnson (D), served 1963–1969

Richard M. Nixon (R), served January 1969–August 9, 1974 (resigned)

Gerald R. Ford (R), served 1974–1977

James E. Carter (D), served 1977–1981

Ronald W. Reagan (R), served 1981–1989

George H.W. Bush (R), served 1989–1993

William J. Clinton (D), served 1993–2001

George W. Bush (R), served 2001–Present

Seven presidents served one-year terms under the Articles of Confederation before George Washington was the first president elected under the new Constitution. The seven: John Hanson (1781–1782), Elias Boudinot (1782–1783), Thomas Mifflin (1783–1784), Richard Henry Lee (1784–1785), Nathan Gorman (1785–1786), Arthur St. Clair (1786–1787), and Cyrus Griffin (1787–1788).

John Adams and his friend Thomas Jefferson died on the same day—July 4, 1826. Adams died first. His last words were, "Thomas Jefferson still survives."

Thomas Jefferson liked to answer the White House door himself—often in slippers.

James Buchanan was the only bachelor president.

Grover Cleveland was the only president to serve two non-consecutive terms.

In 1906, Teddy Roosevelt was the first president to receive a Nobel Peace Prize, for mediating a peace agreement between Russia and Japan. Woodrow Wilson was the second: he won in 1919 for creating the League of Nations.

At 6'4" and over 300 lbs, William Howard Taft was our biggest president.

Sheep grazed on Woodrow Wilson's White House lawn during WW I. Their wool was sold to profit the Red Cross.

FDR was the only president elected to three terms.

JFK was America's first Catholic president.

Gerald Ford and his wife, Betty, worked as models before they married.

Jimmy Carter was the first American president born in a hospital.

FROM

PAUL REVERE'S RIDE

HENRY WADSWORTH LONGFELLOW, 1860 (SET IN 1775)

LISTEN, MY CHILDREN, AND YOU SHALL HEAR
OF THE MIDNIGHT RIDE OF PAUL REVERE,
ON THE EIGHTEENTH OF APRIL, IN SEVENTY-FIVE;
HARDLY A MAN IS NOW ALIVE
WHO REMEMBERS THAT FAMOUS DAY AND YEAR.

HE SAID TO HIS FRIEND, "IF THE BRITISH MARCH
BY LAND OR SEA FROM THE TOWN TO-NIGHT,
HANG A LANTERN ALOFT IN THE BELFRY ARCH
OF THE NORTH CHURCH TOWER AS A SIGNAL LIGHT,——
ONE, IF BY LAND, AND TWO, IF BY SEA;
AND I ON THE OPPOSITE SHORE WILL BE,
READY TO RIDE AND SPREAD THE ALARM
THROUGH EVERY MIDDLESEX VILLAGE AND FARM,
FOR THE COUNTRY FOLK TO BE UP AND TO ARM."

THEN HE SAID, "GOOD NIGHT!" AND WITH MUFFLED OAR
SILENTLY ROWED TO THE CHARLESTOWN SHORE,
JUST AS THE MOON ROSE OVER THE BAY,
WHERE SWINGING WIDE AT HER MOORINGS LAY
THE SOMERSET, BRITISH MAN-OF-WAR;

A PHANTOM SHIP, WITH EACH MAST AND SPAR
ACROSS THE MOON LIKE A PRISON BAR,
AND A HUGE BLACK HULK, THAT WAS MAGNIFIED
BY ITS OWN REFLECTION IN THE TIDE.

MEANWHILE, HIS FRIEND, THROUGH ALLEY AND STREET,
WANDERS AND WATCHES WITH EAGER EARS,
TILL IN THE SILENCE AROUND HIM HE HEARS
THE MUSTER OF MEN AT THE BARRACK DOOR,
THE SOUND OF ARMS, AND THE TRAMP OF FEET,
AND THE MEASURED TREAD OF THE GRENADIERS,
MARCHING DOWN TO THEIR BOATS ON THE SHORE.

THEN HE CLIMBED THE TOWER OF THE OLD NORTH CHURCH,
BY THE WOODEN STAIRS, WITH STEALTHY TREAD,
TO THE BELFRY-CHAMBER OVERHEAD,
AND STARTLED THE PIGEONS FROM THEIR PERCH
ON THE SOMBRE RAFTERS, THAT ROUND HIM MADE
MASSES AND MOVING SHAPES OF SHADE,—
BY THE TREMBLING LADDER, STEEP AND TALL,
TO THE HIGHEST WINDOW IN THE WALL,
WHERE HE PAUSED TO LISTEN AND LOOK DOWN
A MOMENT ON THE ROOFS OF THE TOWN,
AND THE MOONLIGHT FLOWING OVER ALL....

A MOMENT ONLY HE FEELS THE SPELL

OF THE PLACE AND THE HOUR, AND THE SECRET DREAD

OF THE LONELY BELFRY AND THE DEAD;

FOR SUDDENLY ALL HIS THOUGHTS ARE BENT

ON A SHADOWY SOMETHING FAR AWAY,

WHERE THE RIVER WIDENS TO MEET THE BAY,—

A LINE OF BLACK THAT BENDS AND FLOATS

ON THE RISING TIDE, LIKE A BRIDGE OF BOATS.

MEANWHILE, IMPATIENT TO MOUNT AND RIDE,

BOOTED AND SPURRED, WITH A HEAVY STRIDE

ON THE OPPOSITE SHORE WALKED PAUL REVERE.

NOW HE PATTED HIS HORSE'S SIDE,

NOW GAZED AT THE LANDSCAPE FAR AND NEAR,

THEN, IMPETUOUS, STAMPED THE EARTH,

AND TURNED AND TIGHTENED HIS SADDLE-GIRTH;

BUT MOSTLY HE WATCHED WITH EAGER SEARCH

THE BELFRY-TOWER OF THE OLD NORTH CHURCH,

AS IT ROSE ABOVE THE GRAVES ON THE HILL,

LONELY AND SPECTRAL AND SOMBRE AND STILL.

AND LO! AS HE LOOKS, ON THE BELFRY'S HEIGHT

A GLIMMER, AND THEN A GLEAM OF LIGHT!

★ ★ ★

YOU KNOW THE REST. IN THE BOOKS YOU HAVE READ,
HOW THE BRITISH REGULARS FIRED AND FLED,—
HOW THE FARMERS GAVE THEM BALL FOR BALL,
FROM BEHIND EACH FENCE AND FARM-YARD WALL,
CHASING THE RED-COATS DOWN THE LANE,
THEN CROSSING THE FIELDS TO EMERGE AGAIN
UNDER THE TREES AT THE TURN OF THE ROAD,
AND ONLY PAUSING TO FIRE AND LOAD.

SO THROUGH THE NIGHT RODE PAUL REVERE;
AND SO THROUGH THE NIGHT WENT HIS CRY OF ALARM
TO EVERY MIDDLESEX VILLAGE AND FARM,—
A CRY OF DEFIANCE AND NOT OF FEAR,
A VOICE IN THE DARKNESS, A KNOCK AT THE DOOR,
AND A WORD THAT SHALL ECHO FOREVERMORE!
FOR, BORNE ON THE NIGHT-WIND OF THE PAST,
THROUGH ALL OUR HISTORY, TO THE LAST,
IN THE HOUR OF DARKNESS AND PERIL AND NEED,
THE PEOPLE WILL WAKEN AND LISTEN TO HEAR
THE HURRYING HOOF-BEATS OF THAT STEED,
AND THE MIDNIGHT MESSAGE OF PAUL REVERE.

THOMAS JEFFERSON TO JAMES MADISON

PARIS, DECEMBER 20, 1787

Thomas Jefferson was in Paris during the Continental Congress, but received a draft of the document and report of the goings-on from friend James Madison. Jefferson's response, excerpted here, includes a persuasive argument for a bill of rights.

I like much the general idea of framing a government, which should go on of itself, peaceably, without needing continual recurrence to the State legislatures. I like the organization of the government into legislative, judiciary and executive. I like the power given the legislature to levy taxes, and for that reason solely, I approve of the greater House being chosen by the people directly....I am captivated by the compromise of the opposite claims of the great and little States, of the latter to equal, and the former to proportional influence. I am much pleased too, with the substitution of the method of voting by person, instead of that of voting by States; and I like the negative given to the Executive, conjointly with a third of either House....

I will now tell you what I do not like. First, the omission of a bill of rights, providing clearly, and without the aid of sophism, for freedom of religion, freedom of the press, protection against standing armies, restriction of monopolies, the eternal and unremitting force of the habeas corpus laws, and trials by jury in all matters of fact triable by the laws of the land, and not by the laws of nations....I have a right to nothing, which another has a right to take away; and Congress will have a right to take away trials by jury in all civil cases. Let me add, that a bill of rights is what the people are entitled to against every government on earth, general or particular, and what no just government should refuse, or rest on inference....

At all events, I hope you will not be discouraged from making other trials, if the present one should fail. We are never permitted to despair of the commonwealth. I have thus told you freely what I like, and what I dislike, merely as a matter of curiosity; for I know it is not in my power to offer matter of information to your judgment, which has been formed after hearing and weighing everything which the wisdom of man could offer on these subjects. I own, I am not a friend to a very energetic government. It is always oppressive. It places the governors

indeed more at their ease, at the expense of the people. The late rebellion in Massachusetts has given more alarm, than I think it should have done. Calculate that one rebellion in thirteen States in the course of eleven years, is but one for each State in a century and a half. No country should be so long without one. Nor will any degree of power in the hands of government, prevent insurrections....Educate and inform the whole mass of the people. Enable them to see that it is their interest to preserve peace and order, and they will preserve them. And it requires no very high degree of education to convince them of this. They are the only sure reliance for the preservation of our liberty. After all, it is my principle that the will of the majority should prevail. If they approve the proposed constitution in all its parts, I shall concur in it cheerfully, in hopes they will amend it, whenever they shall find it works wrong. This reliance cannot deceive us, as long as we remain virtuous; and I think we shall be so, as long as agriculture is our principal object, which will be the case, while there remains vacant lands in any part of America. When we get piled upon one another in large cities, as in Europe, we shall become corrupt as in Europe, and go to eating one another as they do there....

Th: Jefferson

THE STAR-SPANGLED BANNER

FRANCIS SCOTT KEY, 1814

Oh, say can you see by the dawn's early light
What so proudly we hail'd at the twilight's last gleaming,
Whose broad stripes and bright stars through the perilous fight,
O'er the ramparts we watch'd, were so gallantly streaming?
And the rockets' red glare, the bombs bursting in air,
Gave proof through the night that our flag was still there.
Oh say does that star-spangled banner yet wave
O'er the land of the free and the home of the brave?

On the shore dimly seen through the mists of the deep,
Where the foe's haughty host in dread silence reposes,
What is that which the breeze, o'er the towering steep,
As it fitfully blows, half conceals, half discloses?
Now it catches the gleam of the morning's first beam,
In full glory reflected now shines on the stream:
'Tis the star-spangled banner, oh, long may it wave
O'er the land of the free and the home of the brave!

And where is that band who so vauntingly swore
That the havoc of war and the battle's confusion
A home and a country should leave us no more?
Their blood has wash'd out their foul footstep's pollution.
No refuge could save the hireling and slave
From the terror of flight or the gloom of the grave,
And the star-spangled banner in triumph doth wave
O'er the land of the free and the home of the brave.

Oh, thus be it ever, when freemen shall stand
Between their lov'd home and the war's desolation!
Blest with vict'ry and peace may the heav'n-rescued land
Praise the Power that hath made and preserv'd us a nation!
Then conquer we must, when our cause it is just,
And this be our motto, "In God is our trust."
And the star-spangled banner in triumph wave
O'er the land of the free and the home of the brave!

APPLE PIE

Apple Pie was originally created by English settlers as a variation on the English meat pie. I discovered this extraordinary version at *Zin* in Sonoma County, California. Chef Jeff Mall explained that the recipe belonged to his mother, Barbara McBride. It is a perennial on his menu.

Piecrust

2 cups sifted all-purpose flour

1-teaspoon salt

²/₃ cup solid vegetable shortening, chilled

6–8 tablespoons ice water

1. Sift the flour and salt together into a mixing bowl. Cut the vegetable shortening into the flour with a pastry blender (or two knives), until the mixture resembles coarse meal.

2. Sprinkle the ice water in a little at a time, blending it quickly into the dough.

3. Wrap the dough lightly in waxed paper and place it in the refrigerator for 30 minutes.

Pie Filling

5 Gravenstein apples, peeled, cut in half, and sliced $1/2''$ thick

$2/3$ cup sugar

3 tablespoons ground cinnamon

about 2 tablespoons lime juice
(1 or 2 limes, juiced)

3 tablespoons "Laird's Apple Jack" apple brandy

$1/2$ stick unsalted butter, diced

1 tablespoon heavy cream

sugar for dusting pie crust

1. Preheat oven to 400° F.

2. Divide the dough in half, roll out the bottom piecrust, and place in a 9″ round pie plate.

3. Place a third of the apples on the piecrust. Sprinkle with a third of the sugar, 1 teaspoon ground cinnamon, 1 tablespoon lime juice, and 1 tablespoon apple brandy. Dot the apples with a third of the diced butter. Repeat, starting with the rest of the apples.

4. Roll out the top piecrust and place over the top of the pie. Crimp the edges together, and poke steam vents in the top of the pie.

5. Brush the top with cream, sprinkle it with sugar, and place the pie on a cookie sheet. Slide it into the preheated oven.

6. Bake at 400° F for 15–20 minutes until filling starts to bubble.

7. Lower the heat to 350° F and cook for 20 minutes more.

Let the pie cool slightly and serve with vanilla ice cream.

Serves 6 to 8.

The Civil War

When anti-slavery president Abraham Lincoln was elected, seven states seceded to form the Confederate States of America, with its own constitution and president, Jefferson Davis. On April 12, 1861 Davis' troops attacked the Union-held Fort Sumter in South Carolina, firing the shots that began the war.

Despite pressure, Lincoln insisted the war was more about preserving the Union than fighting slavery. After the battle at Antietam in September 1862, he reconsidered and issued the Emancipation Proclamation.

The first legal African-American regiment was the 54th Massachusetts. Many others followed: in all, 179,000 African Americans served in the Civil War.

William Tecumseh Sherman (1820–1891) led 100,000 Union troops through Georgia, leaving destruction in his wake.

Posing as a Confederate sympathizer, Virginian Elizabeth Van Lew passed information to the North. "Crazy Bet" also arranged prison escapes and hid fugitives.

At least 620,000 Americans died fighting the Civil War—that's more than in all wars America's fought since then, combined.

The Battle of Gettysburg was the bloodiest of the war. Approximately 23,000 Union and 28,000 Confederate soldiers died before the North declared victory.

Other major battles included Shiloh (24,000 killed) in April 1862, Second Manassas (25,000 killed) in August 1862, Chancellorsville (30,000 killed) in May 1863, and The Battle of the Wilderness (25,000 killed) in May 1864.

The Civil War ended on April 9, 1865, with the Confederates' surrender at Appomattox, in Virginia.

The Civil War created more than 400,000 morphine-addicted veterans.

Robert E. Lee (1807–1870) commanded the Confederate forces. He led victories at Bull Run, Fredericksburg and Chancellorsville, before surrendering at Appomattox.

Confederate President Jefferson Davis (1808–1889) was a congressman, war hero and secretary of war. He lost his citizenship after the war.

Ulysses S. Grant's (1822–1885) controversial leadership of the Union army caused heavy losses but won the war. He negotiated the South's surrender, and—as our 18th president—presided over the reconstruction.

Confederate commander Thomas J. "Stonewall" Jackson (1824–1863) gained his nickname organizing troops into a line which withstood the Union assault at Bull Run. He died of injuries accidentally inflicted by his own men.

THE GETTYSBURG ADDRESS

ABRAHAM LINCOLN
GETTYSBURG, PENNSYLVANIA, NOVEMBER 19, 1863

FOUR SCORE AND SEVEN YEARS AGO our fathers brought forth on this continent a new nation, conceived in liberty, and dedicated to the proposition that all men are created equal.

Now we are engaged in a great civil war, testing whether that nation or any nation so conceived and so dedicated can long endure. We are met on a great battle-field of that war. We have come to dedicate a portion of that field as a final resting place for those who here gave their lives that that nation might live. It is altogether fitting and proper that we should do this.

But in a larger sense, we cannot dedicate—we can not consecrate, we can not hallow—this ground. The brave men, living and dead, who struggled here, have consecrated it, far above our poor power to add or detract. The world will little note nor long remember what we say here, but it can never forget what they did here. It is for us the living, rather, to be dedicated here to the unfinished work which they who fought here have thus far so nobly advanced. It is rather for us to be here dedicated to the great task remaining before us—that from these honored dead we take increased devotion to that cause for which they gave the last full measure of devotion—that we here highly resolve that these dead shall not have died in vain—that this nation under God, shall have a new birth of freedom—and that government of the people, by the people, for the people shall not perish from the earth.

YANKEE DOODLE

ANONYMOUS, 1775

Father and I went down to camp
Along with Captain Goodwin,
And there we saw the men and boys
As thick as hasty pudding.

Chorus
Yankee Doodle, keep it up,
Yankee Doodle dandy!
Mind the music and the steps,
And with the girls be handy!

There was Captain Washington
Upon a slapping stallion,
Giving orders to his men,
I guess there was a million.

And there they had a swamping gun
As big as a log of maple,

On a deuced little cart,
A load for father's cattle.

And every time they fired it off,
It took a horn of powder;
It made a noise like father's gun,
Only a nation louder.

And there I saw a little keg,
Its heads were made of leather—
They knocked upon it with little sticks
To call the folks together.

The troopers, too, would gallop up
And fire right in our faces,
It scared me almost half to death
To see them run such races.

But I can't tell you half I saw;
They kept up such a smother,
So I took off my hat, made a bow,
And scampered home to mother.

THE PLEDGE OF ALLEGIANCE

OFFICIALLY ADOPTED ON FLAG DAY, JUNE 14 1924
("UNDER GOD" AMENDMENT MADE BY CONGRESS IN 1954)

I pledge allegiance to the flag
of the United States of America
and to the republic for which it stands;
one nation under God, indivisible,
with liberty and justice for all.

African Americans

Born Isabella Baumfree, Sojourner Truth (1797–1883) was a New York slave freed when the state abolished slavery in 1828. She walked throughout the country speaking against slavery.

Frederick Douglass (1818–1895) was an escaped slave whose speeches were instrumental in the issuance of the Emancipation Proclamation.

Harriet Tubman (1820–1913) was a crucial figure in the Underground Railroad; an escaped slave herself, she risked her life to help bring more than 300 slaves into Canada.

Former slave Booker T. Washington (1856–1915) became a prominent educator and orator. In his position as advisor to two presidents, he was an early advocate of black self-reliance.

W. E. B. DuBois (1863–1963) was the first black to get a Ph.D. from Harvard. He later co-founded the National Association for the Advancement of Colored People (NAACP).

Edward Kennedy "Duke" Ellington (1899–1974) was a pianist, composer, bandleader and musical arranger who defined the sound of jazz with his complex and swinging melodies.

Thurgood Marshall (1908–1993) successfully argued the landmark *Brown v. Board of Education* for the NAACP. He went on to become the first African American Supreme Court Justice.

By refusing to give her bus seat to a white man in 1955, Rosa Parks (1913–) became the embodiment of resistance to the South's Jim Crow laws. Her gesture sparked a bus boycott that galvanized the civil rights movement.

In 1950 Gwendolyn Brooks (1917–2000) became the first black to win a Pulitzer Prize for her poetry collection, *Annie Allen*.

Known as the "First Lady of Song," Ella Fitzgerald's (1918–1996) interpretations defined the great jazz composers. She was also a visionary in the art of scat-singing—playing her voice like an instrument, with impeccable rhythm and pitch.

After a brief prison term, Malcolm Little became Malcolm X (1925–1965)—a leader of the Nation of Islam who preached black unity and empowerment. In 1964, he converted to orthodox Islam. He was assassinated by former Nation of Islam comrades a year later.

The Reverend Martin Luther King, Jr. (1929–1968) was an inspiring civil rights leader. He won the 1964 Nobel Peace Prize for advocating non-violence as the path to social change.

Talk show queen Oprah Winfrey (1954–) is one of the richest people in America. The award-winning media mogul and philanthropist also acts, edits her own magazine and produces films.

FROM
RENASCENCE

EDNA ST. VINCENT MILLAY, 1917

ALL I COULD SEE FROM WHERE I STOOD
WAS THREE LONG MOUNTAINS AND A WOOD;
I TURNED AND LOOKED ANOTHER WAY,
AND SAW THREE ISLANDS IN A BAY.
SO WITH MY EYES I TRACED THE LINE
OF THE HORIZON, THIN AND FINE,
STRAIGHT AROUND TILL I WAS COME
BACK TO WHERE I'D STARTED FROM;
AND ALL I SAW FROM WHERE I STOOD
WAS THREE LONG MOUNTAINS AND A WOOD.

OVER THESE THINGS I COULD NOT SEE:
THESE WERE THE THINGS THAT BOUNDED ME.
AND I COULD TOUCH THEM WITH MY HAND,
ALMOST, I THOUGHT, FROM WHERE I STAND.

AND ALL AT ONCE THINGS SEEMED SO SMALL
MY BREATH CAME SHORT, AND SCARCE AT ALL.
BUT, SURE, THE SKY IS BIG, I SAID:
MILES AND MILES ABOVE MY HEAD;
SO HERE UPON MY BACK I'LL LIE
AND LOOK MY FILL INTO THE SKY.
AND SO I LOOKED, AND AFTER ALL,
THE SKY WAS NOT SO VERY TALL.
THE SKY, I SAID, MUST SOMEWHERE STOP.
AND—SURE ENOUGH!—I SEE THE TOP!
THE SKY, I THOUGHT, IS NOT SO GRAND;
I'MOST COULD TOUCH IT WITH MY HAND!
AND REACHING UP MY HAND TO TRY,
I SCREAMED TO FEEL IT TOUCH THE SKY.

FROM
ADVENTURES OF HUCKLEBERRY FINN
MARK TWAIN, 1885

WE HAD MOUNTAINS on the Missouri shore and heavy timber on the Illinois side, and the channel was down the Missouri shore at that place, so we warn't afraid of anybody running across us. We laid there all day and watched the rafts and steamboats spin down the Missouri shore, and up-bound steamboats fight the big river in the middle....

When it was beginning to come on dark, we poked our heads out of the cottonwood thicket and looked up, and down, and across; nothing in sight; so Jim took up some of the top planks of the raft and built a snug wigwam to get under in blazing weather and rainy, and to keep the things dry. Jim made a floor for the wigwam, and raised it a foot or more above the level of the raft, so now the blankets and all the traps was out of the reach of steamboat waves. Right in the middle of the wigwam we made a layer of dirt about five or six inches deep with a frame around it for to hold it to its place; this was to build a fire on in sloppy weather or chilly; the wigwam would keep it from being seen. We made an extra steering oar, too, because one of the others might get broke, on a snag or something. We fixed up a short forked stick to hang the old lantern on; because we must always light the lantern whenever we see a steamboat coming down stream, to keep from getting run over; but we wouldn't have to light it for up-stream boats unless we see we was in what they call a "crossing"; for the river was pretty high yet, very low banks being still a little under water; so up-bound boats didn't always run the channel, but hunted easy water.

This second night we run between seven and eight hours, with a current that was making over four mile an hour. We catched fish, and talked, and we took a swim now and then to keep off sleepiness. It was kind of solemn, drifting down the big still river, laying on our backs looking up at the stars, and we didn't ever feel like talking loud, and it warn't often that we laughed, only a little kind of a low chuckle. We had might good weather, as a general thing, and nothing ever happened to us at all, that night, nor the next, nor the next.

ADVENTURES OF HUCKLEBERRY FINN

Every night we passed towns, some of them away up on black hillsides, nothing but just a shiny bed of lights, not a house could you see. The fifth night we passed St. Louis, and it was like the whole world lit up. In St. Petersburg they used to say there was twenty or thirty thousand people in St. Louis, but I never believed it till I see that wonderful spread of lights at two o'clock that still night. There warn't a sound there; everybody was asleep.

Every night, now, I used to slip ashore, towards ten o'clock, at some little village, and buy ten or fifteen cents' worth of meal or bacon or other stuff to eat; and sometimes I lifted a chicken that warn't roosting comfortable, and took him along. Pap always said, take a chicken when you get a chance, because if you don't want him yourself you can easy find somebody that does, and a good deed ain't ever forgot. I never see pap when he didn't want the chicken himself, but that is what he used to say, anyway.

Mornings, before daylight, I slipped into corn fields and borrowed a watermelon, or a mushmelon, or a punkin, or some new corn, or things of that kind. Pap always said it warn't no harm to borrow things, if you was meaning to pay them back, sometime; but the widow said it warn't anything but a soft name for stealing, and no decent body would do it. Jim said he reckoned the widow was partly right and pap was partly right; so the best way would be for us to pick out two or three things from the list and say we wouldn't borrow them anymore—then he reckoned it wouldn't be no harm to borrow the others. So we talked it over all one night, drifting along down the river, trying to make up our minds whether to drop the watermelons, or the cantelopes, or the mushmelons, or what. But towards daylight we got it all settled satisfactory, and concluded to drop crab-apples and p'simmons. We warn't feeling just right, before that, but it was all comfortable now. I was glad the way it come out, too, because crabapples ain't ever good, and the p'simmons wouldn't be ripe for two or three months yet.

We shot a water-fowl, now and then, that got up too early in the morning or didn't go to bed early enough in the evening. Take it all around, we lived pretty high.

World War I

In 1914, tensions already building in Europe came to a head when Archduke Francis Ferdinand of Austria-Hungary was assassinated in Sarajevo by a Serb nationalist. A month later, the world was at war.

America's declared stance of neutrality was severely strained after German subs torpedoed the passenger ship *Lusitania* on May 1, 1915, killing over a thousand people, 123 of them Americans. The tide of public opinion was irreversibly shifted.

Forsaking its own policy of isolationism, America declared war on Germany on April 6, 1917, three years after the war began. The war ended less than a year later.

When the war began, the American air force had just 12 officers, 54 enlisted men and fewer than a dozen planes.

13,000 women (known as Yeomanettes) served with the Navy and Marine Corps in WWI, with the same status as men.

Writers Ernest Hemingway, John Dos Passos, e.e. cummings, W. Somerset Maugham and Dashiell Hammett all served as ambulance drivers during WWI. Gertrude Stein also volunteered medical assistance.

Mustard gas, named for its color and odor, was used later in the war; a blistering agent, it acted with severity on any exposed, moist skin.

WWI innovations—such as trench warfare, tanks and airplanes—changed the way war was fought. Instead of the isolated battles of the past, war was waged on fronts that stretched for miles.

Other WWI inventions included poison gas, first used by the Germans on April 22, 1915, in France. The ensuing five-mile cloud, composed of 168 tons of chlorine gas, resulted in widespread panic and death.

The war's end came at the low point of German resources and morale. Woodrow Wilson's Fourteen Points were accepted as general terms for Germany's surrender on November 11, 1918.

More than 9 million soldiers died in the war. 117,000 of them were Americans.

Best known for having led the first U.S. troops into France, General John Joseph Pershing (1860–1948) held degrees from a teaching academy, West Point and the University of Nebraska's law school. Among his military innovations was the National Guard.

Some 750 poets, playwrights, writers, artists, architects and composers were killed in WWI.

AMERICA

Samuel Francis Smith, 1831

My country, 'tis of thee,
Sweet land of liberty,
Of thee I sing;
Land where my fathers died,
Land of the Pilgrim's pride,
From ev'ry mountainside
Let freedom ring!

My native country, thee,
Land of the noble free,
Thy name I love;
I love thy rocks and rills,
Thy woods and templed hills;
My heart with rapture thrills,
Like that above.

Let music swell the breeze,
And ring from all the trees
Sweet freedom's song.
Let mortal tongues awake;
Let all that breathe partake;
Let rocks their silence break,
The sound prolong.

Our father's God, to Thee,
Author of liberty,
To Thee we sing.
Long may our land be bright
With freedom's holy light;
Protect us by Thy might,
Great God, our King!

State Capitals

NC
SC
NJ
NY
V
NE
G
M
P

UNITE OR DIE

Olympia ✪ WASHINGTON

Salem ✪

OREGON

Helena ✪ MONTANA

Boise ✪ IDAHO

WYOMING

NEVADA

Sacramento ✪

Carson City ✪

✪ Salt Lake City

Cheyenn

CALIFORNIA

UTAH

Denver

COLORAD

ARIZONA

Santa Fe ✪

NEW MEXICO

Phoenix ✪

ALASKA

Juneau ✪

Honolulu ✪

HAWAII

"The Only Thing We Have to Fear Is Fear Itself"

Franklin Delano Roosevelt
Washington, D. C., March 4, 1933

In his inaugural address to a nation still reeling from the Great Depression, Franklin Delano Roosevelt conveyed a bold sense of hope and a steely resolve.

THIS IS A DAY OF NATIONAL CONSECRATION, and I am certain that my fellow-Americans expect that on my induction into the Presidency I will address them with a candor and a decision which the present situation of our nation impels.

This is preeminently the time to speak the truth, the whole truth, frankly and boldly. Nor need we shrink from honestly facing conditions in our country today. This great nation will endure as it has endured, will revive and will prosper.

So first of all let me assert my firm belief that the only thing we have to fear is fear itself—nameless, unreasoning, unjustified terror which paralyzes needed efforts to convert retreat into advance.

In every dark hour of our national life a leadership of frankness and vigor has met with that understanding and support of the people themselves which is essential to victory. I am convinced that you will again give that support to leadership in these critical days.

In such a spirit on my part and on yours we face our common difficulties. They concern, thank God, only material things. Values have shrunken to fantastic levels; taxes have risen; our ability to pay has fallen; government of all kinds is faced by serious curtailment of income; the means of exchange are frozen in the currents of trade; the withered leaves of industrial enterprise lie on every side; farmers find no markets for their produce; the savings of many years in thousands of families are gone.

More important, a host of unemployed citizens face the grim problem of existence, and an equally great number toil with little return. Only a foolish optimist can deny the dark realities of the moment.

Yet our distress comes from no failure of substance. We are stricken by no plague of locusts. Compared with the perils which our forefathers conquered because they believed and were not afraid, we have still much to be thankful for. Nature still offers her bounty and human efforts have multiplied it. Plenty is at our doorstep, but a generous use of it languishes in the very sight of the supply.

Our greatest primary task is to put people to work. This is no unsolvable problem if we face it wisely and courageously.

It can be accomplished in part by direct recruiting by the government itself, treating the task as we would treat the emergency of a war, but at the same time, through this employment, accomplishing greatly needed projects to stimulate and reorganize the use of our natural resources....

Finally, in our progress toward a resumption of work we require two safeguards against a return of the evils of the old order; there must be a strict supervision of all banking and credits and investments; there must be an end to speculation with other people's money, and there must be provision for an adequate but sound currency....

We do not distrust the future of essential democracy. The people of the United States have not failed. In their need they have registered a mandate that they want direct, vigorous action.

They have asked for discipline and direction under leadership. They have made me the present instrument of their wishes. In the spirit of the gift I take it.

In this dedication of a nation we humbly ask the blessing of God. May He protect each and every one of us! May He guide me in the days to come!

World War II

General George S. Patton (1885–1945) was nicknamed "Old Blood and Guts." Commanding the U.S. Third Army in Europe, he won a pivotal battle when he and his men drove the Germans back from France after the D-Day landings.

The U.S. was officially neutral until December 7, 1941, when the Japanese attacked Pearl Harbor. At dawn on Sunday, 360 planes attacked in two waves, sinking 16 ships and killing 2,400 military and civilian Americans.

On December 8, 1941, the U.S. declared war on Japan; similar declarations were made against Germany and Italy three days later.

Bob Hope is the only civilian to be made an "Honorary Veteran" for his work entertaining the troops— "G.I. Bob" traveled 30,000 miles to perform for over one million troops in 1945 alone.

During WWII, The Office of Censorship banned baseball announcers from any mention of weather conditions during their broadcasts for fear that enemies wanting to attack the city would receive valuable information.

Norman Rockwell's *Saturday Evening Post* cover depicting "Rosie the Riveter" (May 29, 1943) epitomized the spirit of the nearly 3 million women who entered war work, replacing men called into the armed forces.

On August 6, 1945, the American bomber *Enola Gay* dropped the first atomic bomb on Hiroshima, Japan, destroying 4.4 square miles. Three days later a second atomic bomb landed on Nagasaki. The two attacks killed and wounded more than 200,000. Japan sued for peace the next day.

Champion chess player Reuben Fine helped the war effort by calculating, on the basis of positional probability, where enemy submarines might surface.

More than 500 native Navajo "talkers" were enlisted by the Marines to serve in the Pacific. Navajo, impossible for the Japanese translate, also saved time because it needed minimal coding.

On April 29, 1945, American troops liberated 27,400 prisoners from the Dachau concentration camp. It's estimated another 50,000 died there.

During wartime sugar rationing, most soda companies scaled back production. Not so 7-UP which, being less sweet, required less sugar. Instead, it cashed in with a national advertising campaign.

It took two surrenders to end WWII. In Europe, Germany surrendered to General Eisenhower on May 7, 1945. But in the Pacific, the Japanese continued fighting until the atomic bomb was dropped, finally surrendering on August 14, 1945.

Of all the Americans who served in the armed forces, 6.6% were killed (407,316) or wounded (670,846).

New England Clam Chowder

There is another version of this chowder, made with a tomato base instead of cream, which goes by the name Manhattan Clam Chowder. The very notion of such a variation is considered a crime in the state of Maine, where they once tried to pass a law against it. Here is the classic recipe.

4 tablespoons butter

2 medium yellow onions, peeled and diced

2 tablespoons white flour

4 cups chicken stock

3 russet potatoes, peeled and diced

4 carrots, peeled and finely diced

1 cup leeks, diced

2 teaspoons fresh thyme leaves

1/4 cup chopped fresh parsley

4 cups shucked cherrystone clams, quartered

2 cups clam juice

1/2 cup half-and-half

1. Heat the butter in a large, heavy pot and sauté the onions over medium-low heat until translucent, about 10 minutes. Sprinkle flour over the onions and cook for another couple of minutes.

2. Add chicken stock slowly, blending as you go, then add the potatoes, carrots, leeks and herbs. Simmer another 10 minutes.

3. Add the clams and the clam juice, reduce heat to low, cover the pot, and slowly simmer until the potatoes are fork tender (another 15 minutes). Add half-and-half and cook another 5 minutes. Serve with oyster crackers.

Serves 8.

LOBSTER ROLLS

This quintessential New England meal actually originated in Connecticut. You have to serve them on hot dog buns to be authentic. They're perfect on a hot summer afternoon with a tall glass of lemonade, or on a cool evening accompanied by a cup of New England Clam Chowder.

3 tablespoons mayonnaise

1 teaspoon Dijon mustard

2 teaspoons diced scallions

2 tablespoons lemon juice

salt and pepper to taste

cooked and chilled lobster meat from two 1 pound lobsters, cut into small chunks

½ cup chopped lettuce (I like iceberg or romaine)

2 celery ribs, finely chopped

4 buttered hot dog rolls

1. Mix mayonnaise, mustard, scallions, lemon juice, salt, and pepper. Then add lobster meat, chopped lettuce, and celery.

2. Place open buttered rolls face down in a hot skillet for about one minute to toast.

3. Fill the hot dog rolls, and feast.

Serves 4.

AMERICA THE BEAUTIFUL

KATHARINE LEE BATES. 1913

O beautiful for spacious skies,
   For amber waves of grain,
For purple mountain majesties
   Above the fruited plain!
America! America!
   God shed His grace on thee
And crown thy good with brotherhood
   From sea to shining sea!

O beautiful for pilgrim feet,
   Whose stern, impassioned stress
A thoroughfare for freedom beat
   Across the wilderness!
America! America!
   God mend thine every flaw,
Confirm thy soul in self-control,
   Thy liberty in law!

O beautiful for heroes proved
   In liberating strife,
Who more than self their country loved,
   And mercy more than life!
America! America!
   May God thy gold refine,
Till all success be nobleness
   And every grain divine!

O beautiful for patriot dream
   That sees beyond the years
Thine alabaster cities gleam
   Undimmed by human tears!
America! America!
   God shed His grace on thee,
And crown thy good with brotherhood
   From sea to shining sea!

Women

Pocahontas (1595–1617), daughter of a powerful Powhatan chief, helped improve Indian-settler relations by saving the life of settler John Smith. She later married Englishman John Rolfe and traveled to Britain, where she died of smallpox.

Dolley Madison (1768–1849) was a young widow when she married 43-year-old James Madison. She saved the original drafts of the Constitution and the Declaration of Independence from a White House fire.

Elizabeth Cady Stanton (1815–1902) was a writer and orator; Susan B. Anthony (1820–1906) a tactician and organizer. Together they influenced the legislation granting women property rights and, ultimately, the vote.

Elizabeth Blackwell (1821–1910) was the first American woman to earn a medical degree.

Red Cross founder Clara Barton's (1821–1912) fame grew from her campaign to provide care and medical supplies to wounded Civil War soldiers.

Planned Parenthood founder Margaret Sanger (1879–1966) educated women about birth control, campaigned to make methods available, and suffered censorship, jail and lawsuits.

Elected to the House in 1916, Montanan Jeannette Rankin (1880–1973) was America's first congresswoman.

※

Devoted to helping others, First Lady Eleanor Roosevelt (1884–1962) campaigned for human, women's, and civil rights, and for the young, the poor and democracy.

※

Amelia Earhart (1897–1937), the first woman passenger to fly the Atlantic, later flew it solo—in a record 14 hours, 56 minutes. In 1937, she vanished during an attempt to fly around the world.

※

Colonel Oveta Culp Hobby (1905–1995) was the first female army colonel. Appointed to create a place in the army for women, she led the newly-created Women's Army Corps.

※

Betty Friedan (1921–) wrote *The Feminine Mystique*, founded the National Organization for Women

(NOW) and fought for the Equal Rights Amendment.

※

Marilyn Monroe (1926–1962) was one of the 20th century's most famous faces. Christened Norma Jeane Baker, she starred in such films as *Some Like it Hot* and *The Misfits*.

※

Singer Leontyne Price (1927–) debuted at the Metropolitan Opera House in 1961. Her honors include 18 Grammys and the Presidential Medal of Freedom.

※

First Lady Jacqueline Bouvier Kennedy Onassis (1929–1994), infused the White House with style. After her husband's assassination, she moved to New York with her children and became a book editor.

※

As a writer, journalist and activist for women's rights, Gloria Steinem (1934–) founded *Ms. Magazine*.

FROM
"ASK NOT WHAT YOUR COUNTRY CAN DO FOR YOU"

JOHN F. KENNEDY, WASHINGTON, D.C., JANUARY 20, 1961

At 43, John F. Kennedy was the youngest president elected in U.S. history. In his inaugural address, he called for a patriotic brand of action.

WE OBSERVE TODAY not a victory of party but a celebration of freedom—symbolizing an end as well as a beginning—signifying renewal as well as change. For I have sworn before you and Almighty God the same solemn oath our forebears prescribed nearly a century and three quarters ago.

The world is very different now. For man holds in his mortal hands the power to abolish all forms of human poverty and all forms of human life. And yet the same revolutionary beliefs for which our forebears fought are still at issue around the globe—the belief that the rights of man come not from the generosity of the state but from the hand of God.

We dare not forget today that we are the heirs of that first revolution. Let the word go forth from this time and place, to

friend and foe alike, that the torch has been passed to a new generation of Americans—born in this century, tempered by war, disciplined by a hard and bitter peace, proud of our ancient heritage—and unwilling to witness or permit the slow undoing of those human rights to which this Nation has always been committed, and to which we are committed today at home and around the world.

Let every nation know, whether it wishes us well or ill, that we shall pay any price, bear any burden, meet any hardship, support any friend, oppose any foe to assure the survival and the success of liberty....

In your hands, my fellow citizens, more than mine, will rest the final success or failure of our course. Since this country was founded, each generation of Americans has been summoned to give testimony to its national loyalty. The graves of young Americans who answered the call to service surround the globe.

Now the trumpet summons us again—not as a call to bear arms, though arms we need—not as a call to battle, though embattled we are—but a call to bear the burden of a long twilight struggle, year in and year out, "rejoicing in hope, patient in tribulation"—a struggle against the common enemies of man: tyranny, poverty, disease and war itself.

Can we forge against these enemies a grand and global alliance, North and South, East and West, that can assure a more fruitful life for all mankind? Will you join in that historic effort?

In the long history of the world, only a few generations have been granted the role of defending freedom in its hour of maximum danger. I do not shrink from this responsibility—I welcome it. I do not believe that any of us would exchange places with any other people or any other generation. The energy, the faith, the devotion which we bring to this endeavor will light our country and all who serve it—and the glow from that fire can truly light the world.

And so, my fellow Americans: Ask not what your country can do for you—ask what you can do for your country.

My fellow citizens of the world: Ask not what America will do for you, but what together we can do for the freedom of man.

Finally, whether you are citizens of America or citizens of the world, ask of us here the same high standards of strength and sacrifice which we ask of you. With a good conscience our only sure reward, with history the final judge of our deeds, let us go forth to lead the land we love, asking His blessing and His help, but knowing that here on earth God's work must truly be our own.

Vietnam

American determination to stem the spread of communism in Asia led to direct involvement in Vietnam when the first American "advisors" arrived in 1955.

✳

The U.S. Air Force first deployed the defoliant Agent Orange (named for its orange metal containers) in 1962, in an effort to expose Vietcong trails and roads.

✳

Covert U.S. and South Vietnamese naval operations began in early 1965. "Operation Rolling Thunder"—sustained bombing raids of North Vietnam—began in February and continued for three years.

✳

The first Marines arrived in Danang, Vietnam in 1965.

✳

Protests weren't just for radicals and hippies: as early as 1966, veterans of World Wars I and II and the Korean War rallied in New York against American involvement in Vietnam.

✳

Recruiters from Dow Chemical, the manufacturer of Napalm, were driven from the University of Wisconsin at Madison in 1967, amid massive student protests.

✳

On January 31, 1968, the North Vietnamese launched the surprise Tet Offensive. Though U.S. forces ultimately pushed back the communists, the event revealed how badly America had underestimated the Vietcong.

Charlie Company, 11th Brigade, American Division, slaughtered more than 300 civilians in the village of My Lai on March 16, 1968. A shocked America only learned of the infamous massacre a year later. Commanding officer Lt. William Calley was convicted of murder in 1971.

"Operation Breakfast" was a covert bombing campaign in Cambodia ordered by President Nixon in 1969, without the knowledge of Congress or the American people.

On May 4, 1970, four students were killed and eight others wounded when National Guardsmen opened fire on an antiwar demonstration at Ohio's Kent State University.

The New York Times published the Pentagon Papers in 1971. Leaked from inside the government, they detailed years of deception by the U.S. military and the White House concerning America's policy in Vietnam.

Nixon ordered the demobilization of 70,000 troops 1972. In 1973, Henry Kissinger and North Vietnam's Le Duc Tho signed a cease-fire agreement. Congressional hearings on the bombing of Cambodia resulted in an order to stop all such bombings on August 15, 1973.

The last American troops were evacuated from Saigon in 1975, as the city fell to communist forces.

For the U.S., the war produced more than 2 million veterans, took more than 58,000 lives and cost more than $150 billion.

WILLIAM LEDERER TO
ADMIRAL DAVID McDONALD

1962

William Lederer is the co-author of The Ugly American *(1958), which portrayed the boorish side of Americans overseas. Four years after its publication, he had an experience while traveling in France with his family that prompted his writing to the Chief of U.S. Naval Operations.*

Admiral David L. McDonald, USN
Chief of Naval Operations
Washington, D.C.

Dear Admiral McDonald,

*E*ighteen people asked me to write this letter to you.

Last year at Christmas time, my wife, three boys and I were in France, on our way from Paris to Nice. For five wretched days everything had gone wrong. Our hotels were "tourist traps," our rented car broke down; we were all restless and irritable in the crowded car. On Christmas Eve, when we checked into our hotel in Nice, there was no Christmas spirit in our hearts.

It was raining and cold when we went out to eat. We found a drab little restaurant shoddily decorated for the holiday. Only five tables were occupied. There were two German couples, two French families, and an American sailor, by himself. In the corner a piano player listlessly played Christmas music.

I was too tired and miserable to leave. I noticed that the other customers were eating in stony silence. The only person who seemed happy was the American sailor. While eating, he was writing a letter, and a half-smile lighted his face.

My wife ordered our meal in French. The waiter brought us the wrong thing. I scolded my wife for being stupid. The boys defended her, and I felt even worse.

Then, at the table with the French family on our left, the father slapped one of his children for some minor infraction, and the boy began to cry.

On our right, the German wife began berating her husband....Through the front door came an old flower woman. She wore a dripping, tattered overcoat, and shuffled in on wet, rundown shoes. She went from one table to the other.

"Flowers, monsieur? Only one franc."

No one bought any.

Wearily she sat down at a table between the sailor and us. To the waiter she said, "A bowl of soup. I haven't sold a flower all afternoon." To the piano player she said hoarsely, "Can you imagine, Joseph, soup on Christmas Eve?"

He pointed to his empty "tipping plate."

The young sailor finished his meal and got up to leave. Putting on his coat, he walked over to the flower woman's table.

"Happy Christmas," he said, smiling and picking out two corsages. "How much are they?"

"Two francs, monsieur."

Pressing one of the small corsages flat, he put it into the letter he had written, then handed the woman a 20-franc note.

"I don't have change, monsieur," she said. "I'll get some from the waiter."

"No, ma'am," said the sailor, leaning over and kissing the ancient cheek. "This is my Christmas present to you."

Then he came to our table, holding the other corsage in front of him. "Sir," he said to me, "may I have permission to present these flowers to your beautiful daughter?"

In one quick motion he gave my wife the corsage, wished us a Merry Christmas and departed.

Everyone had stopped eating. Everyone had been watching the sailor. Everyone was silent.

A few seconds later Christmas exploded throughout the restaurant like a bomb.

The old flower woman jumped up, waving the 20-franc note, shouted to the piano player, "Joseph, my Christmas present! And you shall have half so you can have a feast too."

94

The piano player began to belt out *Good King Wencelaus*, beating the keys with magic hands.

My wife waved her corsage in time to the music. She appeared 20 years younger. She began to sing, and our three sons joined her, bellowing with enthusiasm.

"*Gut! Gut!*" shouted the Germans. They began singing in German.

The waiter embraced the flower woman. Waving their arms, they sang in French.

The Frenchman who had slapped the boy beat rhythm with his fork against a bottle. The lad climbed on his lap, singing in a youthful soprano.

A few hours earlier 18 persons had been spending a miserable evening. It ended up being the happiest, the very best Christmas Eve, they had ever experienced.

This, Admiral McDonald, is what I am writing you about. As the top man in the Navy, you should know about the very special gift that the U.S. Navy gave to my family, to me and to the other people in that French restaurant. Because your young sailor had Christmas spirit in his soul, he released the love and joy that had been smothered within us by anger and disappointment. He gave us Christmas.

Thank you, Sir, very much.

Merry Christmas,
Bill Lederer

The New Colossus

Emma Lazarus, 1883

inscribed on The Statue of Liberty in 1901

Not like the brazen giant of Greek fame,
With conquering limbs astride from land to land;
Here at our sea-washed, sunset gates shall stand
A mighty woman with a torch, whose flame
Is imprisoned lightning, and her name
Mother of Exiles. From her beacon-hand
Glows world-wide welcome; her mild eyes command
The air-bridged harbor that twin cities frame.
"Keep, ancient lands, your storied pomp!" cries she
With silent lips. "Give me your tired, your poor,
Your huddled masses yearning to breathe free,
The wretched refuse of your teeming shore.
Send these, the homeless, tempest-tost to me,
I lift my lamp beside the golden door!"